I Love Trains!

A TENDER is pulled behind a steam engine to carry extra water or coal.

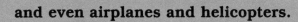

FLATCARS carry cars, boats, trucks, and even airplanes and helicopters.

GONDOLA CARS can carry scrap metal, like old cars and stoves.

The CABOOSE was a place for the train's conductor to sleep.

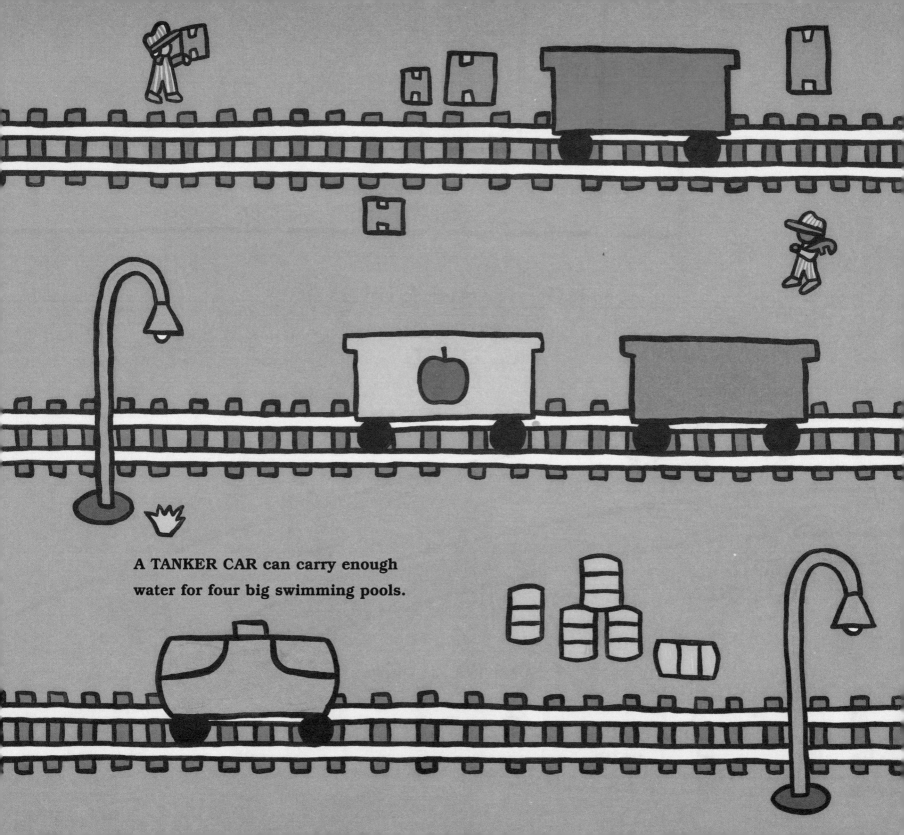

A TANKER CAR can carry enough
water for four big swimming pools.

Trains, trains, trains!

I LOVE trains!

I wave.

I'm glad

to see the car that carries Dad.

But the best car's at the end,
and as the train goes round the bend,

or secret stuff that's under wrap.

Some carry steel; some carry scrap,

or logs.

or gas

or hogs

or cows

Some cars carry trucks or grain,

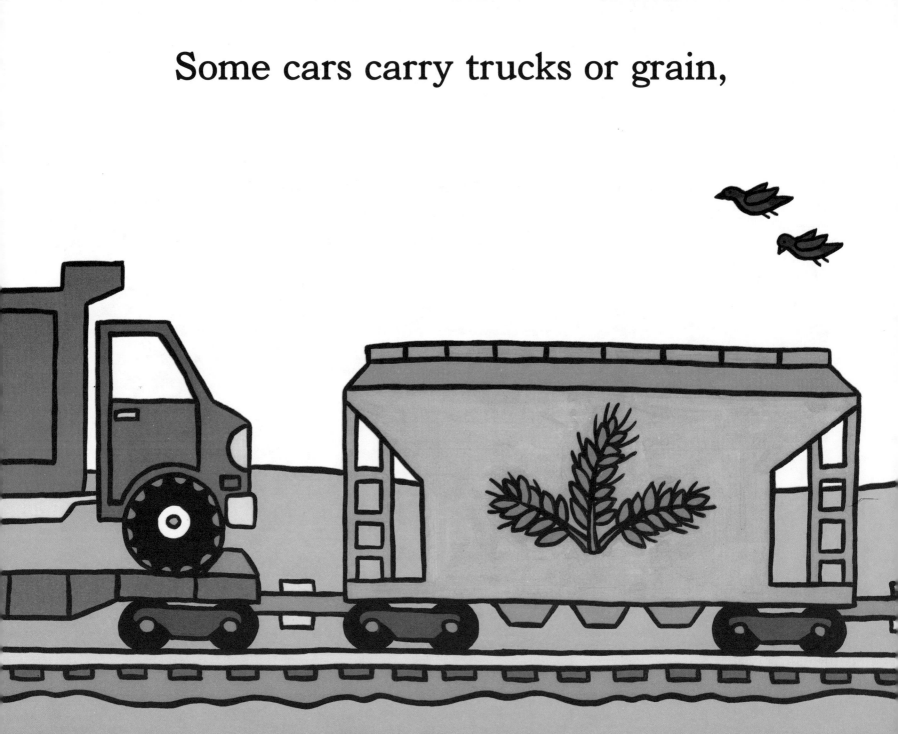

Some cars keep things from the rain.

pulling lots of cars along.

First come engines, big and strong,

I like trains that hoot and roar
as they rumble by my door.

Trains, trains, trains! I like trains.

I Love Trains!

BY **Philemon Sturges**

ILLUSTRATED BY **Shari Halpern**

SCHOLASTIC INC.

New York Toronto London Auckland Sydney
Mexico City New Delhi Hong Kong Buenos Aires

*To Shari, who loves trains as much as
I do, and to her new child, who will
soon be reading about them*

—P.S.

For Jane

—S.H.

ISBN 0-439-41805-4

Text copyright © 2001 by Philemon Sturges.
Illustrations copyright © 2001 by Shari Halpern.
All rights reserved.
Published by Scholastic Inc., 557 Broadway, New York, NY 10012,
by arrangement with HarperCollins Publishers.
SCHOLASTIC and associated logos are trademarks and/or
registered trademarks of Scholastic Inc.

12 11 10 9 8 7   4 5 6 7/0

Printed in the U.S.A.   08

First Scholastic printing, September 2002

A HOPPER CAR can carry enough grain to feed a horse for eight months.

BOXCARS often carry cows, horses, or pigs.